Help Hungry HENRY Deal with ANGER

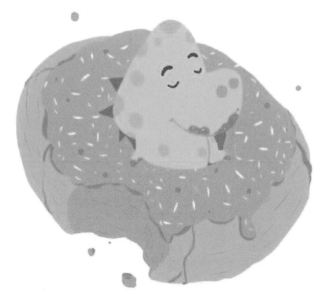

First Printing, 2020
ISBN 978-3-948298-12-8

Do you see Hungry Henry?
What is he doing?
Let's ask him.

Tap Hungry Henry on the shoulder.

Hungry Henry seems upset. Let's find out what he is doing to see if we can help. Can this telescope help us find out?

Wipe the telescope clean to have a look!

I think I know what Hungry Henry is trying to do. Hungry Henry is building a rocket. **How cool!**

But Hungry Henry is so angry. Let's help him to calm down.

"Hungry Henry, you are angry!"

I'm not angry - maybe you are angry! I'm the calmest of us all.

"Hungry Henry, I notice that you are clenching your fists and your voice is loud. Your angrymeter shows that you are at a level 8. Can we help by finding a snack for you?"

ANGRYMETER

Tap the snack so Hungry Henry can find it.

"Much better. It's okay to be angry, but please try not to break things."

"Before we put the nozzle on the engine, let's try Rocket Breathing.

Raise your arms above your head and say, '**Rocket Up**,' and breathe in.

Then say, '***Rocket Down,***' and breathing out
and slowly bringing your arms back down."

Now ALL!

Check the angrymeter.
It's working! **Yes - you did it!**"

"You can do it. Say it! '*I can do it. I can do it.*'"

I can do it.
I can do it!

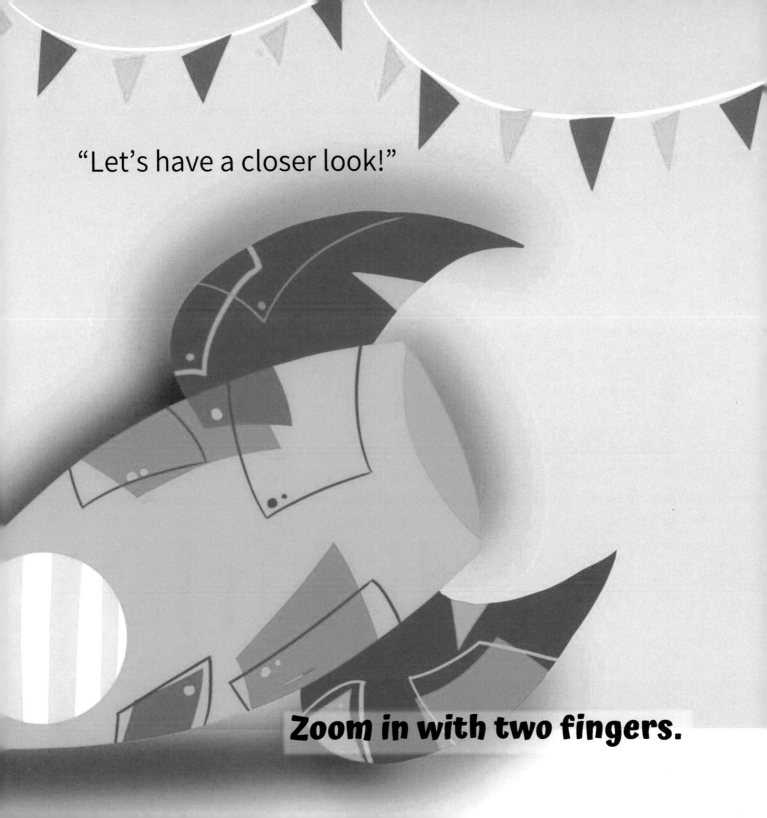

The rocket is hungry, like me. It needs food to take off into space. I can't find any fuel.

Tap the fuel can to help Hungry Henry.

What is Henry doing over there?
Quick, we need another snack!

Tilt the book to the right to help Hungry Henry to get the snack.

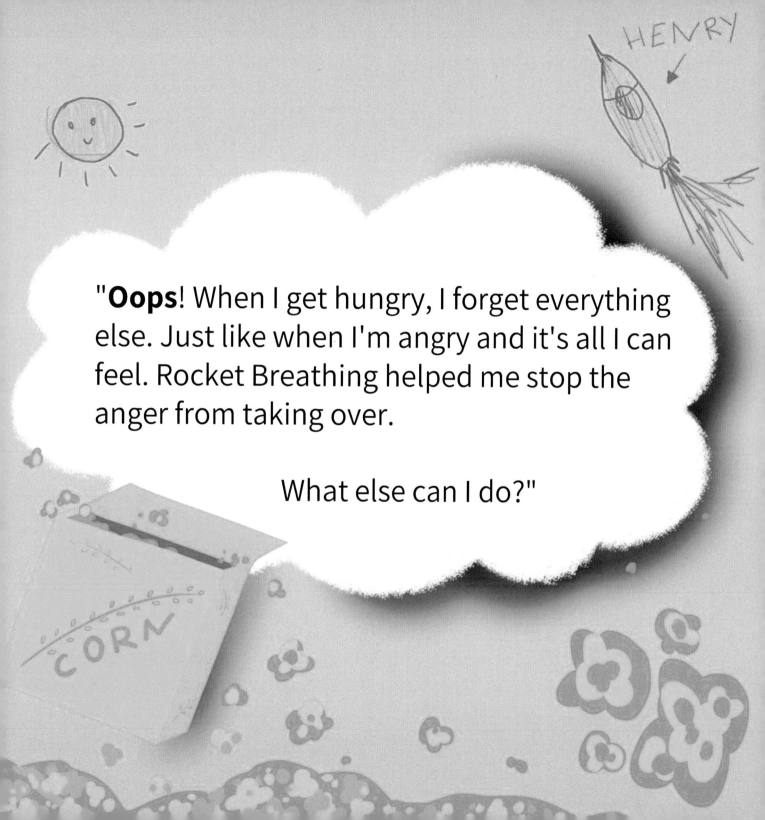

"You could count down from 10 like a rocket launch.

Or you could repeat something in your mind over and over again. **'*I can do this. I can do this. I can do this.*'**

You could even color or read a book.

What do you think
would work for you?"

Things look ready. Hungry Henry, it's time to fly.

My gift for you: Color and Grow coloring book for **FREE** instead of $6.99:

free.powerofyet.com/henry

Please go to Amazon and **leave a review** to spread the word about Hungry Henry and to support an indie author.
Thanks, Esther

★ ★ ★ ★ ★

Power
of
YET

Growth Mindset Series

I Can't Do That, YET

Enna is a girl who doesn't believe in herself and often utters the phrase "I can't do that!"

She develops a growth mindset throughout the story and learns to say, "I can't do that YET!".

A World without Failures

A world without mistakes.
Amazing or horrible?

After reading this story, children realize that mistakes are a good thing and are important for successful learning.

Your Thoughts Matter

Your child's mindset matters, *more than they realize.* 'Your Thoughts Matter' gives concrete examples of what different mindsets sound like in our heads.
'This is too hard; I'll never learn it.' vs *'It's meant to be hard; we grow by challenging ourselves.'*

Little Bears Can Do Big Things

Is it okay for boys to feel afraid? Is it okay for them to need help? Of course it is.

A sweet father and son story about being brave.

Made in the USA
Middletown, DE
07 May 2021